Contents

*S = silver; G = gold; P = platinum; ( ) = the line must be played but cannot be assessed for a Medal.

Mr T.C.'s Banana Boat

Phil Croydon

AB 3035

Puppet Dance

Philip Sparke

Baker Street Blues

Nick Breeze

AB 3035

Iron Man

James Rae

AB 3035

Motor Madness

John Miller

Barbara Allen

Trad. arr. Neil Butterworth

AB 3035

Cheese and Pickled Onions

Op. 176d

Derek Bourgeois

You've Been Trumped!

Robert Tucker

AB 3035

Ragbag

Philip Harper

AB 3035

Peter on the Sea

Spiritual arr. Guy Woolfenden

AB 3035

Brass-Bell Boogie

Stephen Roberts

AB 3035

The Truth

James Rae

AB 3035

Pastime with Good Company

Henry VIII arr. Stephen Roberts

AB 3035

The Foggy, Foggy Dew

Trad. **English** arr. John Frith

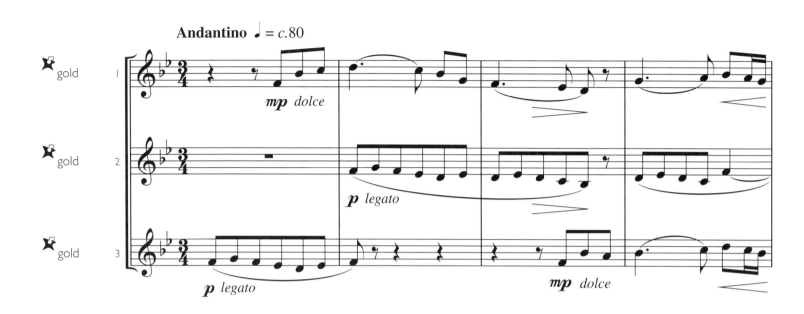

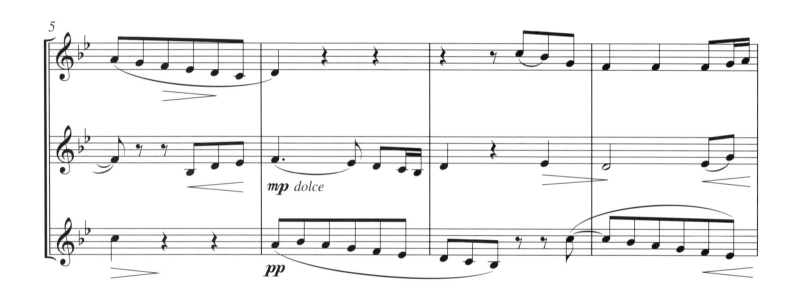

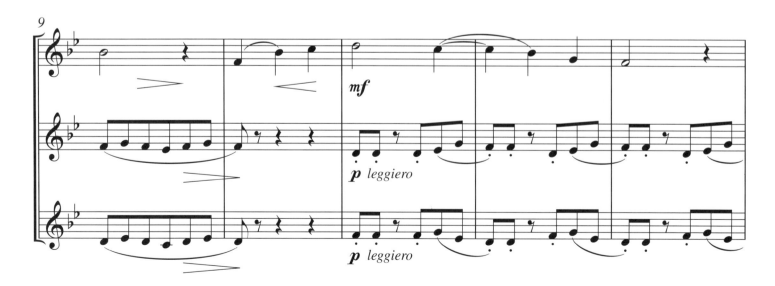

AB 3035

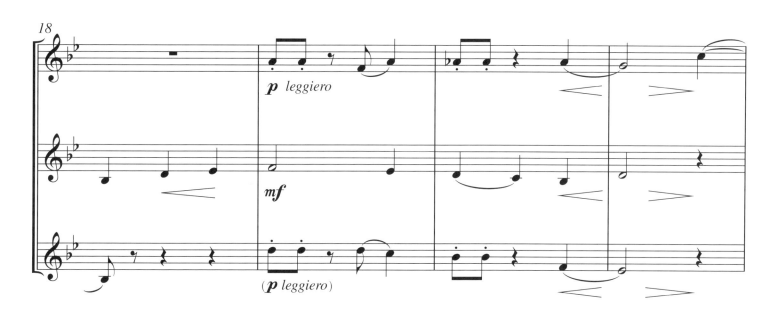

Rain Dance

Stephen Roberts

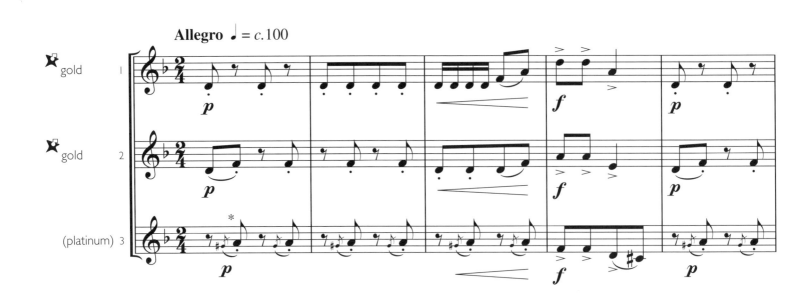

* Use third valve for A.

The Camptown Races

S. C. Foster arr. James Rae

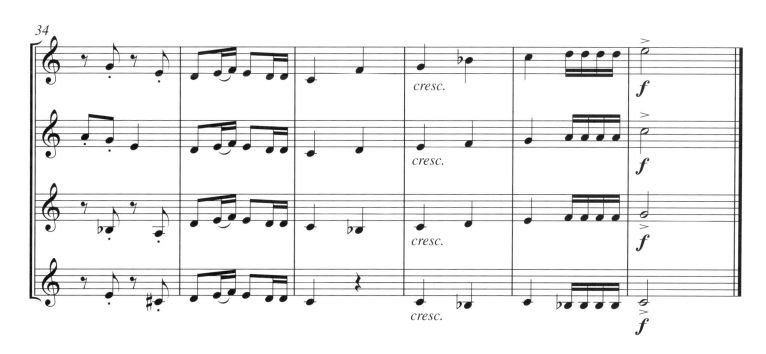

The Minute Minuet

Philip Harper

AB 3035

Tarantella

Philip Sparke

AB 3035

Chase!

Paul Harris

AB 3035

Rock for Four

Nick Breeze

AB 3035

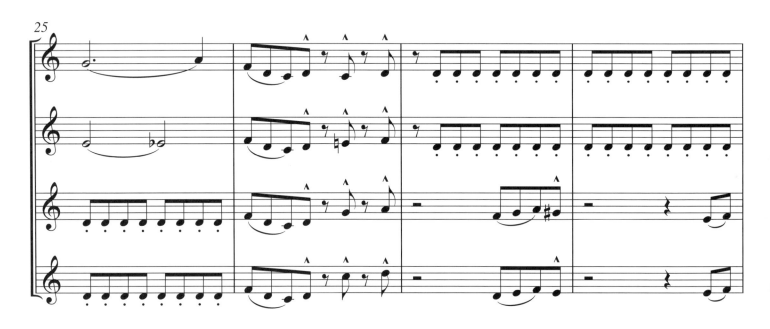

AB 3035